INSIDE THE
Royal Tyrrell Museum
of Palaeontology

INSIDE THE
Royal Tyrrell Museum
of Palaeontology

Royal Tyrrell Museum Cooperating Society
Drumheller, Alberta, Canada

The Royal Tyrrell Museum Cooperating Society © 2010
Published in Canada

Library and Archives Canada Cataloguing in Publication

> *Inside the Royal Tyrrell Museum of Palaeontology.*

Includes bibliographical references and index.
ISBN 978-0-9697292-3-5

> *1. Tyrrell Museum of Palaeontology—Guidebooks. 2. Tyrrell*
Museum of Palaeontology—History. 3. Palaeontology—Alberta.
I. Tyrrell Museum of Palaeontology

QE716.C32D7 2010   560.74'71233   C2010-903701-4

Images on Front Cover and Section Dividers

> *top: George F. Sternberg uncovering a*
> *dinosaur in the badlands, Steveville, Alberta,*
> *1920. Glenbow Archives NA-3250-7*

> *middle: Fossilized* Gorgosaurus *skeleton*
> *on display at the Royal Tyrrell Museum.*
> *Thedor Erkamps and Owen Melenka*

> *bottom: Hiker in Alberta badlands.*
> *Royal Tyrrell Museum Library Collection*

Printed in Canada

ROYAL TYRRELL
MUSEUM
Cooperating Society

*Set in the fossil-rich Alberta badlands,
the Royal Tyrrell Museum brings
the science of palaeontology to life—
inspiring curiosity and wonder.*

Book developed by

The Royal Tyrrell Museum of Palaeontology
Drumheller, Alberta, Canada

Lisa Making – Head, Strategic Initiatives
Sue Sabrowski – Visual Asset Coordinator and Photographer
Kathryn Valentine – Director, Exhibits and Communications

and

Brown Bag Design
Calgary, Alberta, Canada

Joan Bailey – Managing Editor and Creative Director
Anna Rebus – Researcher and Author
Jeffrey Gibson – Graphic Designer

Contributors
Edna Barker
Laura Bourgeault
Thedor Erkamps
Teresa McLaren
Owen Melenka
Frances Purslow

*Information contained in this publication
is accurate as of May 2010.*

ISBN 978-0-9697292-3-5

Contents

Foreword

When I was growing up in central Alberta, very few people knew what palaeontology was. Of course, we knew about dinosaurs, but they weren't a large part of the public consciousness. Today, however, the word palaeontology is part of our vernacular, and a worldwide fascination with dinosaurs means that many people know about the riches of Alberta's badlands.

Much of this shift can be attributed to a few brave adventurers, such as J.B. Tyrrell, who spent time in western Canada setting the stage for the *Great Canadian Dinosaur Rush* of the early 1900s. Alberta was central in the development of the science of palaeontology—a role that led to the establishment of the Royal Tyrrell Museum of Palaeontology in 1985.

The Museum is an icon for fossil enthusiasts around the world. Our breathtaking landscape and fossil-rich surroundings are only the beginning; we are stewards of the fossils we hold in trust. Our Museum is where fossils are collected, prepared, stored, studied, curated, and admired. The Royal Tyrrell Museum of Palaeontology welcomes some of the top research scientists in the world and more than 400,000 visitors a year.

Here, our award-winning exhibits and innovative educational programming constantly evolve to accommodate this ever-changing science. We strive to make our collection as accessible as possible in a friendly, welcoming, and immersive environment.

Today we remain committed to our original goal—to celebrate the 3.9 billion years of life on planet Earth.

We are very proud of this book, a celebration of curiosity, truth, and wonder. Sincere thanks to everyone involved in its creation.

Andrew Neuman
Executive Director
Royal Tyrrell Museum of Palaeontology
2010

I have no special talents.
I am only passionately curious.
ALBERT EINSTEIN

Unearthing Palaeontology in Alberta

Alberta's Red Deer River valley, home to the Royal Tyrrell Museum, is one of the most exceptional fossil sites in the world.

A World of Fossils

While the origins of the science of palaeontology date back centuries, the term palaeontology was first coined in 1822 to refer to the study of ancient living organisms through fossils.[1] This science helps us discover more about our world in the prehistoric past, while fostering in us a greater understanding about the world we live in today.[2]

[1]

In a few exceptional places—
such as Alberta's badlands—
erosion has exposed an abundance
of fossils at the Earth's surface.

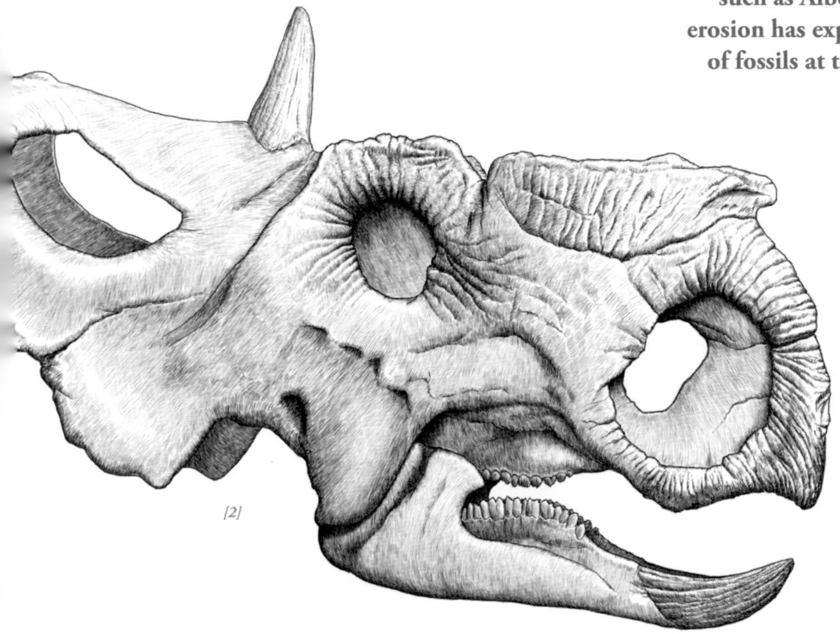

[2]

[**fig 1, 2**] Phalarodon *skeleton, and* Pachyrhinosaurus *skull.*

[**fig 3**] *Map of Red Deer River valley.*

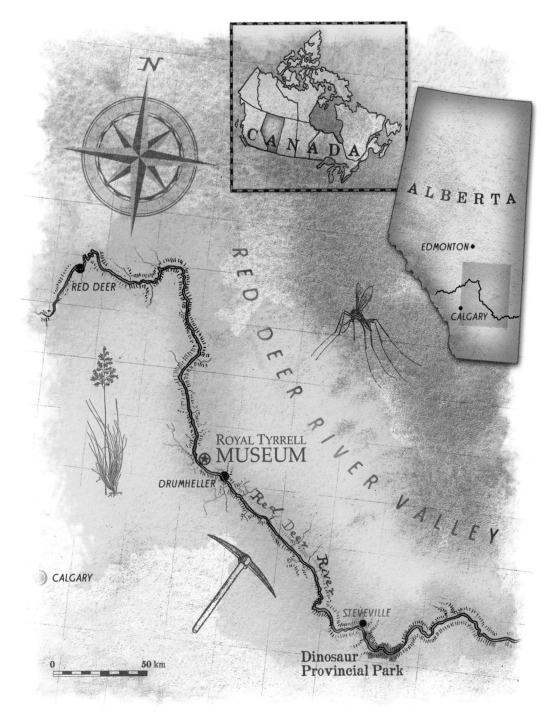

N

CANADA

ALBERTA

EDMONTON •

CALGARY •

RED DEER

RED DEER RIVER VALLEY

ROYAL TYRRELL
MUSEUM

DRUMHELLER

Red Deer River

CALGARY

STEVEVILLE

Dinosaur
Provincial Park

0   50 km

[4]

What is a Fossil?

Fossils are the remains and traces of ancient, once-living organisms. As a rule, a specimen qualifies as a fossil when it is more than 10,000 years old.

There are a number of different ways organisms become fossils. To fossilize, the remains of dead plants or animals must be rapidly buried. Bones, scales, teeth and shells preserve well and are abundant in the fossil record. Soft body parts such as skin, muscle tissue and organs decompose quickly and are often consumed by predators before fossilization can take place. Evidence of living organisms such as burrows, tracks, and skin impressions can also be preserved—these are called trace fossils.

Of all the millions of species that evolved and lived on this planet since life first began—of all the billions upon billions of individual organisms—very few have been preserved as fossils.

In 1842, Sir Richard Owen, a British anatomist, coined the term _dinosauria_, meaning "terrible lizard." [3]

[5]

[fig 4] *Sir Richard Owen holding leg bones of a Moa, an extinct flightless bird from New Zealand, ca. 1846.*

[fig 5] *Jean-Baptiste L'Heureux standing with members of the Blackfoot Confederacy [seated, left to right] One Spot, Red Crow, North Axe, mid 1880s.*

[fig 6] *Illustration: cross section of ammonite fossil.*

Grandfather of the Buffalo

The human interest in fossils is not a modern "invention;" in fact, people have been recording their observations about fossils for thousands of years.

In North America, oral traditions, archaeological sites, and encounters with early explorers all bear witness that First Nations people discovered and revered fossils long before others began searching for bones in Alberta's badlands.[4]

Alberta's Niitsitapi (Blackfoot Confederacy) people's word for fossilized ammonites is *iniskim* or "buffalo calling stone." For countless generations, they used these fossils in ceremonies to ensure a successful bison hunt. In the late 1800s, Quebecois priest Jean-Baptiste L'Heureux lived as a translator with the Piikani (Peigan) in southeast Alberta.[5] When his Piikani hosts showed him fossils eroded out of the Red Deer River bank, he wrote of their explanation: "The natives say that the grandfather of the buffalo is buried here."[6]

[6]

Go West Young Adventurers

In the late 1800s, mapmakers, geologists, and surveyors began making their way west to assess Canada's natural resources. They explored the Red Deer River valley when the province of Alberta was still a vast land called the North West Territories, District of Alberta. During their quest, they left no stone unturned and discovered unusual ancient bones. Curiosity transformed these adventurous men into the first fossil collectors in Alberta.

[7]

[8]

[**fig 7**] *Transporting fossils by horse and cart, 1918.*

[**fig 8**] *Sternberg team member Gustav Lindblad with* Chasmosaurus *skull, 1917.*

[**fig 9**] *Canadian 5¢ Registered Mail postage stamp, 1885.*

[**fig 10**] *Now a ghost town, Steveville, Alberta was once a hub of activity—offering fossil hunters a place to collect mail and supplies.*

The Undiscovered Country

In the west at that time, towns were few and far between. Although the train arrived in Calgary in 1883, travel to frontier towns was by horseback, by river or most often, on foot.

Despite the rugged conditions and remote sites, fossil hunters came to the Red Deer River valley to uncover, collect, document, and in certain cases profit from their discoveries. Some came with a sense of adventure, others with a sense of scientific duty, but all left knowing they had experienced an extraordinary place.

[9]

Communication was mainly by mail and it took weeks for correspondence to make its way from these isolated areas back across the country.

[10]

[fig 11] *North American Boundary Commission staff, 1872. Dawson in back row, third from left.*

[fig 12] *Geological Survey of Canada archive stamp.*

[11]

Oh! for a fossil, some poor shell
That died upon an olden shore
But yet in whispered voice can tell
—last hollow throbbing of a bell—
Of the ancient ocean's roar.

A POEM BY G.M. DAWSON [7]

The Little Doctor

One of Canada's earliest scientists to travel west was George Mercer Dawson. He is credited as the first non-First Nations person to discover dinosaur remains in Canada (1874) and is recognized today for his outstanding contributions to science.[8]

A debilitating disease suffered in childhood left Dawson with frequent ill health and stunted growth—earning him the nickname "the little doctor."[9] Despite this, he had an insatiable passion for exploration and discovery.[10]

In 1895, Dawson became director of the Geological Survey of Canada—a post he held until his death in 1901. Three of Canada's national museums trace their roots to the pioneering work of the Geological Survey—the Canadian museums of Nature, Civilization, and Science and Technology.[11]

[13]

J.B. Tyrrell devoted his life
to the exploration of
Canada's natural resources.
The Royal Tyrrell Museum
of Palaeontology
honours his name and
scientific achievements.

[14]

A Fortuitous Find

In 1884, 26-year-old geologist Joseph Burr Tyrrell (1858–1957) made his way west while working for the Geological Survey of Canada (GSC). His job was to seek vast coal deposits for a growing country; his fate would be to discover the first fossil of a meat-eating dinosaur ever found in Canada.

On August 12, 1884, Tyrrell stumbled upon a 70-million-year-old dinosaur skull, the first of its species ever found, just a few kilometres from where the Museum now stands. Although he wasn't a palaeontologist, he realized his discovery was significant.

Over the years, the skull was described by two palaeontologists and named *Albertosaurus sarcophagus* in 1905, the same year Alberta became a province.

In 1898, Tyrrell left the GSC to work as a consultant during the Klondike gold rush. Just over a decade later, the treasure-trove of fossils unearthed in Alberta's badlands by Dawson, Tyrrell and others sparked another type of rush—the *Great Canadian Dinosaur Rush*.

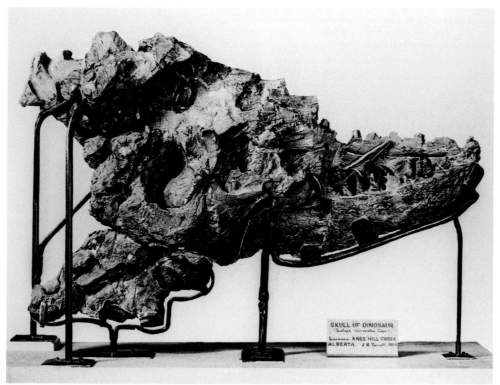

[fig 13, 16] *J.B. Tyrrell was a new breed of explorer—a wilderness traveller who was also a scientist.*[12] *Between 1885 and 1898, he explored and surveyed vast uncharted areas of northwest Canada.*

[fig 14] *The J.B. Tyrrell Historical Medal is an award of the Royal Society of Canada "for outstanding work in the history of Canada."*

[fig 15] *Skull discovered by J.B. Tyrrell. "While down at the bottom of the last coulee, I found a head of one of the large extinct reptiles that used to roam over the country…"*[13]
J.B. Tyrrell, in a letter to his parents, 1884

[16]

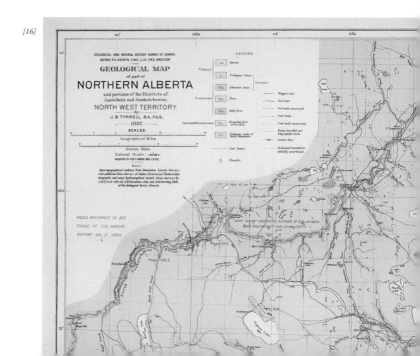

The *Great Canadian Dinosaur Rush*

The *Great Canadian Dinosaur Rush* revolved around two colourful characters—Barnum Brown and Charles H. Sternberg. Lasting from 1910 to 1917, the rush saw thousands of Alberta specimens leave the province— filling the vaults of museums around the world.

Between 1910 and 1915, American Barnum Brown collected many train cars full of fossils in Alberta for the American Museum of Natural History. Of Alberta's bone beds, the *New York Times* reported in 1913: "the field is by no means exhausted; there, erosion is so rapid that for all time the Red Deer River will be classic hunting ground for Cretaceous dinosaurs."

In 1912, in order to stem the flow of valuable fossils out of Canada, the Geological Survey of Canada hired American Charles Hazelius Sternberg to lead a collecting party. Charles H. brought his three sons— Charles M., George, and Levi—with him to Canada. All four Sternbergs had lengthy fossil-related careers. In 1932, Charles M. founded the original Prehistoric Park at the Calgary Zoo.[14] George collected fossils for the University of Alberta. Levi built up a fine fossil collection for the Royal Ontario Museum.

[fig 17] *Packing specimens, Alberta, 1900s.*

[fig 18] *The Sternberg party wearing nets to protect against the "murderous" mosquitos, while travelling on the Red Deer River, 1912.*[15]

[fig 19] *Levi Sternberg jacketing fossil, 1917.*

[fig 20] *John B. Abbott and George Sternberg excavating bones of* Hadrosaur, *1922.*

[17]

*My whole object has been to give
the information I have acquired
through years of toil and hardship
in the desolate fossil fields to the
public, so they may realize something
of the wonders of Nature...*[16]

CHARLES H. STERNBERG, 1917

[19]

[20]

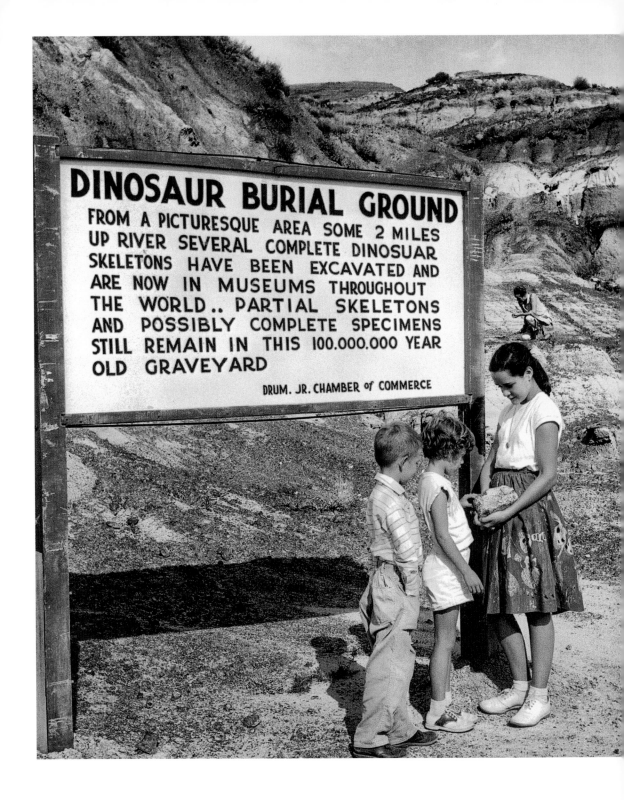

DINOSAUR BURIAL GROUND
FROM A PICTURESQUE AREA SOME 2 MILES UP RIVER SEVERAL COMPLETE DINOSUAR SKELETONS HAVE BEEN EXCAVATED AND ARE NOW IN MUSEUMS THROUGHOUT THE WORLD.. PARTIAL SKELETONS AND POSSIBLY COMPLETE SPECIMENS STILL REMAIN IN THIS 100.000.000 YEAR OLD GRAVEYARD

DRUM. JR. CHAMBER of COMMERCE

[21]

Alberta Fossils Around the World

Fossils found in Alberta during the *Great Canadian Dinosaur Rush* made their way to museums all over the world, including the Natural History Museum in London, England, and the American Museum of Natural History in New York. Alberta fossils also left the province for museums across Canada, including the Royal Ontario Museum in Toronto. During the 1910s, museums in Alberta were not collecting or displaying many locally-found fossils. However, in 1920, the University of Alberta hired George Sternberg to develop a fossil vertebrate collection, which today contains more than 44,000 specimens.

The *Great Canadian Dinosaur Rush* of the early 1900s provided great insight into the world of the Late Cretaceous. Two world wars and the Depression slowed the fossil hunters' pace; however, the science of palaeontology continued to evolve. By the 1970s, shifting attitudes and priorities ignited a renewed interest in Alberta's fossil heritage and many began to wonder how to keep Alberta fossils closer to home.

[fig 21] *Children exploring the Red Deer River valley dinosaur graveyard, 1958.*

Building a
Sense of Place

*The Royal Tyrrell Museum is one of
Canada's premier tourist destinations,
attracting over 400,000 visitors each year
from more than 125 countries.*

Badlands, Good Lands

Floodwaters from melting glaciers carved
the Red Deer River valley more than 10,000
years ago, and subsequent erosion formed
the badlands.

With sparse vegetation, extremes of hot and cold
temperatures, steep slopes and loose soil, the
badlands are notoriously treacherous to travel
through. However, early explorers and fossil
hunters learned quickly that Alberta's badlands
were, in fact, good lands for finding fossils.

Dinosaurs did not
live in harsh and arid badlands.
During the Late Cretaceous
this area was lush and semi-tropical,
with an abundance
of water and plant life.

[fig 22] *Detail from*
Cretaceous Alberta
*exhibit, Royal
Tyrrell Museum.*

[22]

Reading the Rocks

There are three important reasons why
so many dinosaur fossils are found in
Alberta—an abundance of sedimentary
rock, the exposure of these rocks in
the river valleys, and the dry climate.

The rocks you see in the Alberta
badlands were created from sediment
deposited by rivers that flowed between
84 and 65 million years ago, when
dinosaurs roamed the area. Over the
years, as animals died, many were
buried in the river sediments,
eventually becoming fossilized.
Retreating glaciers at the end
of the last ice age stripped the
land bare, exposing fossil-rich
sedimentary rock. With southern
Alberta's dry climate, the rate of
erosion of this rock occurs relatively
quickly, thereby exposing fossils.

The colour variation in the rock
layers of the Alberta badlands
reflects differences in sediments
(and therefore environments).
These layers, called strata, are
like chapters in a book, revealing
stories about life on Earth millions
of years ago.

[24]

[fig 23] *Badlands landscape showing strata, Alberta.*

[fig 24] *Commonly called "popcorn rock." When bentonite clay minerals become wet from rain, they expand 10 times their volume. Later, the surface dries into hard pieces of "popcorn."*

Valley of Riches

The town of Drumheller, Alberta, exists because of the rich coal deposits found in the badlands of the Red Deer River valley.

In the 1950s, Alberta's dependence on coal decreased as many people switched from coal to natural gas to heat their homes. The latter part of the twentieth century witnessed a shift in Drumheller's economy from coal to fossil tourism. The same rocks that yielded coal deposits and shaped the town's growth became an important source of scientific riches that set Drumheller on the path to becoming the dinosaur capital of Canada.

Drumheller residents are justifiably proud of the region's fossil heritage. Even during the quiet years between the *Great Canadian Dinosaur Rush* and the 1970s, valley residents celebrated dinosaurs and made them an integral part of the local culture. Public art, tourist attractions, sports teams, and business names have long reflected a connection to the deep past.

[fig 25] *The Midland Coal Mine, Drumheller area, 1932. The last of Drumheller's coal mines stopped operating in 1979.*

[fig 26] *Calgary kids about to become Dinosaur Soup, Drumheller area campground, 1973.*

[fig 27] *Advertisement for Drumheller Coal, ca. 1970.*

[fig 28] *Painting dinosaur tracks on a Drumheller street, 1958.*

[25]

[26]

[27]

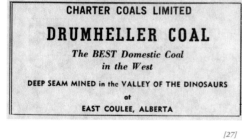

[28]

Breaking New Ground

Interest in local tourism and dinosaurs, along with a desire to keep Red Deer River valley fossils "close to home," led the Alberta government to announce, in 1981, the plan to construct a major new research facility at Drumheller.

Building a Museum in an area riddled with coal mine shafts proved a unique challenge for architects. Although honeycombed with abandoned mine workings, the west end of Midland Provincial Park was eventually deemed suitable for building.[17] Calgary-based architects Bill Boucock Partnership set about creating a design that echoed the layers and colours of the surrounding landscape.

The impressive location and exterior design dictated that the Museum's interior be as remarkable, with thought-provoking and inspiring exhibits to bring Alberta's past to life. An accomplished team was assembled to ensure this would be possible. Palaeontologist Dr. Philip Currie took on the task of building the fossil collection while Dr. David Baird, former Director of the Canadian Museum of Science and Technology, oversaw the development of exhibits and educational programs.

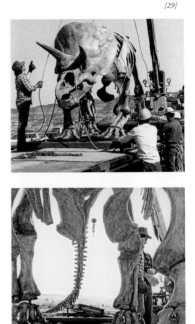

[30]

The Museum is located a few kilometres from J.B. Tyrrell's *Albertosaurus* discovery.

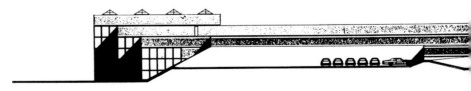

A Museum in the Heart of the Badlands

The Tyrrell Museum of Palaeontology opened
its doors to the world on September 25, 1985.
Queen Elizabeth II bestowed the "royal" designation
in 1990; at that time, the Royal Tyrrell Museum
was one of only three in Canada to have received
such an honour.

[31]

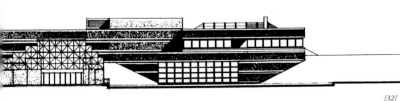

[32]

[**fig 29, 30**] *Moving dinosaur skeletons, 1985.*

[**fig 31**] *Locating the Museum in the heart of the badlands connects visitors to the land in which fossils are unearthed. Hiking trails from the Museum's doorstep give visitors the opportunity to explore this unusual landscape.*

[**fig 32**] *Elevation drawing, 1982.*

Read nature;
nature is a friend to truth.
EDWARD YOUNG

Uncovering
the Science

Fossils, in many cases, are tangible representations of what might otherwise only be dreamed. Giant sauropods, four-winged dinosaurs, enormous fish-like marine reptiles, sabre-toothed cats— all ancient, physical reminders that truth is stranger than fiction—and that this truth is part of an ongoing, elegant natural history.

CRAIG SCOTT Ph.D.
ROYAL TYRRELL MUSEUM SCIENTIST

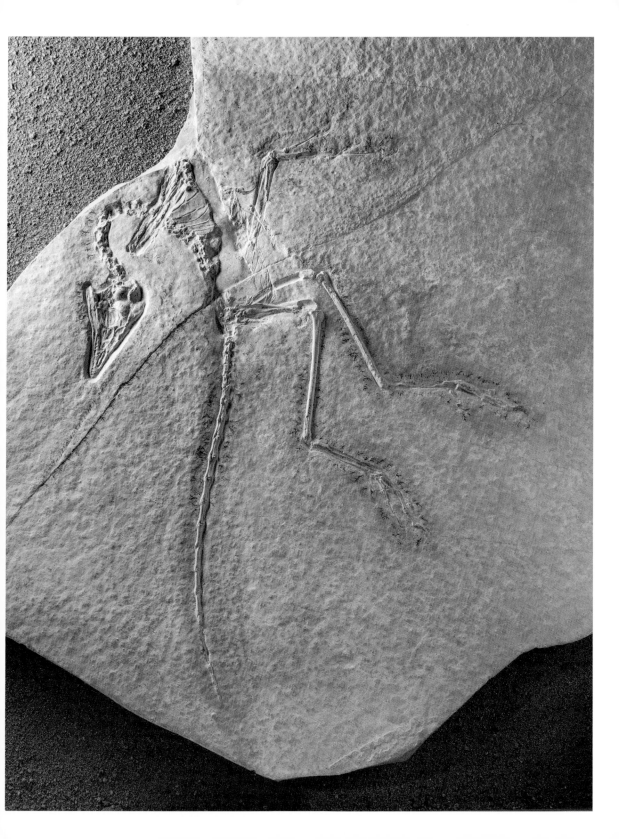

The Science of Palaeontology

All science begins in the imagination—with a sense of wonder and a desire to know how the natural world works.

The Royal Tyrrell Museum has attracted a team of world-renowned scientists committed to uncovering and sharing the history of life on Earth.

Palaeontologists need a vast understanding of a range of fields including biology, chemistry, physics, botany, and geology. Each scientist has a specialty—a specific area of expertise. Through their knowledge, focused research and collaborations, they tackle some of the most daunting mysteries of the natural world.

On their own, each discovery
a scientist makes is important;
put together, they are illuminating.

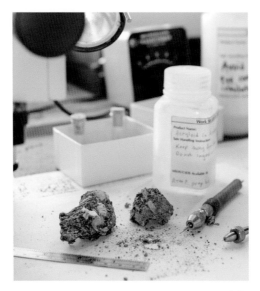

[33]

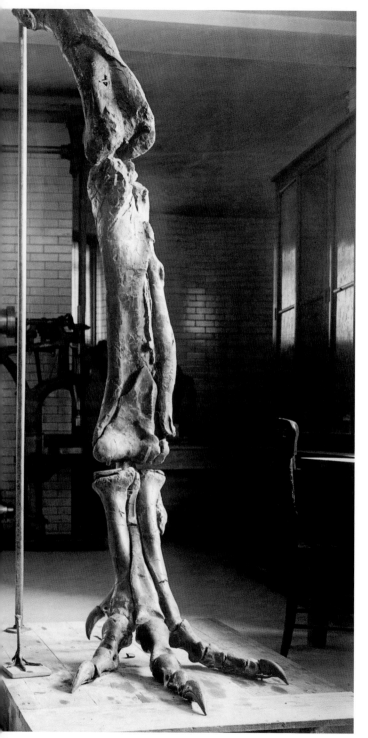

Some palaeontologists study the largest animals that walked the Earth, while others study the smallest.

[35]

[fig 33] *Small fossil specimens in the lab.*

[fig 34] *Leg bones of an* Albertosaurus *found near Steveville, Alberta, ca. 1915.*

[fig 35] *A pollen specimen, magnified and photographed through a microscope,* Accuratipollis macrosolenoides.

[34]

Fieldwork

Royal Tyrrell Museum scientists draw upon their depth and breadth of knowledge during their work both in the field and in the lab. Fieldwork connects scientists to the natural landscape where they search for, and uncover, fossils. Lab work gives scientists time to research and meticulously study their fossil finds.

[36]

Prospecting

The summer field season in Alberta is a time of intense work, new discoveries, and fly-swatting!

Fieldwork is hard, physically demanding work—often taking place in extreme locations and conditions. Scientists hike for hours through rough terrain with eyes firmly trained on the ground. Sometimes a scientist will stumble upon a spectacular find at an unexpected moment—but usually finding fossils is a slow and methodical undertaking.

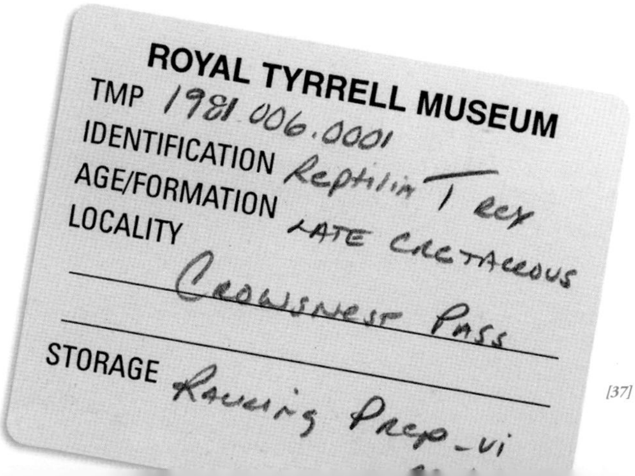

[fig 36] *A quarry marker is used to mark the location of a significant specimen after it has been removed from the rock.*

[fig 37] *A label from the collections area of the Royal Tyrrell Museum, where over 130,000 specimens are catalogued.*

ROYAL TYRRELL MUSEUM

TMP *1981 006.0001*

IDENTIFICATION *Reptilia Trex*

AGE/FORMATION *Late Cretaceous*

LOCALITY

Crowsnest Pass

STORAGE *Rawing Prep - vi*

[37]

[38]

Collecting

When a specimen is found, palaeontologists and technicians first determine how the fossils are positioned in the rock. They dig down to the fossil using picks, shovels, and sometimes jackhammers. Smaller hand tools are used to uncover enough of the specimen to determine its outline, although most of the bone is left unexposed. Then crews dig a trench around the specimen. To protect the fossils from damage, a jacket of burlap and plaster is wrapped around the top and sides of the specimen block and allowed to harden. A layer of tissue paper between the fossil and the jacket keeps plaster from sticking to the bones.

Crews then dig beneath the fossils, adding more plaster and burlap. Eventually, the block sits on a column of rock like a big mushroom. At this stage, the block is ready to be flipped over. Once overturned, the bottom of the block is jacketed and the fossils are ready for transport back to the Museum.

[fig 38] *Occasionally, a specimen is too large or is in too remote a location to be removed by a land vehicle, so it is transported by helicopter.*

The Collection

When specimens arrive at the Museum, they are placed into storage. In some cases, many months or years may elapse before they are moved to the preparation lab. The Museum is home to more than 130,000 individual specimens and more than 2,000 specimens are added to the collection each year.

With such a vast collection, the Museum requires a substantial amount of storage space.

[fig 39] *The surrounding rock has been carefully removed from fossils before they arrive in "prepared storage."*

[fig 40] *Plaster jackets protect fragile fossils in "unprepared storage" while they await preparation and study.*

[39]

[40]

Preparation

The slow task of removing the rock from around the fossil is called preparation. Using a range of tools—from powerful electric hand tools to a simple dental pick—Museum technicians expose the delicate fossil from the surrounding rock. Once prepared, the specimen is ready for study or display.

Why not Collect every Fossil?

Museum scientists collect fossils for one purpose—scientific study. Through planned and deliberate prospecting and intentional collection, a new or rare species, a well-preserved specimen, or a fossil unique to the area may be discovered, providing another glimpse into the prehistoric past.

Collecting fossils requires a significant investment of resources. Scientists spend time prospecting for, uncovering and researching fossils. Once collected, fossils require large areas for storage and preparation. Museum staff also dedicate time to developing displays and education programs. Collecting with a purpose ensures that sufficient time and resources are allocated to preserve Alberta's rich fossil heritage.

[fig 41] *A preparation station with a variety of materials and tools, including toothbrushes, dental picks and adhesives.*

[fig 42] *Effective research requires detailed record keeping, careful storage and thorough documentation.*

Research

Royal Tyrrell Museum scientists conduct their research using the scientific method. They begin with a hypothesis—an idea about why something is the way it is. Next, they gather data and run experiments to test their hypothesis. A scientist might spend years studying a single specimen, comparing it to similar fossils and reviewing results. Identifying the species of a fossil may require many hours of specimen study, referencing publications and drawing comparisons with other fossils in collections around the world. Out of this analysis may come a new understanding—fitting more pieces into the prehistoric puzzle.

It's not what you find, it's what you find out.

DAVID HURST THOMAS,
AMERICAN MUSEUM OF NATURAL HISTORY

Peer Review

Royal Tyrrell Museum scientists present their work to peers in the scientific community for review and critique. This ensures that the research is open and transparent. Timing is critical in this field. Though scientists want to share exciting new ideas, they must be careful not to publish work that has not been verified. Too late, and someone else gets the recognition; too early, and the work may be discredited.

[fig 43] *Palaeontologists often keep detailed field notes to refer to in the lab.*

What's in the Vault?

Some of the specimens in the Museum's collection are so rare and scientifically significant that they are housed in a separate, enclosed, extra-secure storage room.

Among the specimens in the "vault" are 317 holotypes—a term used to describe a specimen that is the first known of its kind anywhere in the world. A holotype can be any type of fossil, and it serves as the name-bearer of the species.

Even if a better specimen is found later, the holotype is not superseded. These are the rare and exciting discoveries that help fill gaps in the fossil record and increase our understanding of ancestry and diversity.

[44]

[fig 44] *The door to the holotype "vault."*

[fig 45] *This giant holotype,* Eotriceratops, *is a species of horned dinosaur discovered in southern Alberta. At 68 million years of age, it is the precursor to* Triceratops. *The skull alone is the size of a grand piano, making it the largest horned dinosaur ever found in Canada, and possibly, the world.*

[45]

Conserving Alberta's Heritage

The fossilized remains of plants and animals, or traces of their activities, are protected under the Government of Alberta's Historical Resources Act which has one of the strictest fossil protection laws in the world. Violation of the Act is punishable by fines of up to $50,000 and/or one year in prison. You can help protect Alberta's fossil heritage by staying on designated hiking trails and informing the Museum of any possible fossil sightings.

Ten minutes of vandalism destroys
all my labor, my hopes, my life almost,
because I can never recover from
such a blow as this.[18]

CHARLES H. STERNBERG, 1917

[fig 46] *George Sternberg and assistant packing fossils, Red Deer River valley, 1921.*

[46]

Collaborating with Industry

Alberta's rich fossil heritage is directly linked to the province's incredible natural resource base, including coal, oil, and gas. Before beginning new projects, companies in these industries contact the Museum to obtain an evaluation of the geological significance of the region under consideration. If anything of historical value is thought to lie within the area, a thorough site investigation is completed.

[48]

[fig 47] *Shiny, black oil seeps from the end of the fossilized tail of* Platypterygius americanus, *a marine reptile.*

[fig 48] *This brass quarry marker was made before the Museum received its "Royal" designation.*

Exploring the Exhibits

Royal Tyrrell Museum exhibits explore the history of life on Earth from the Precambrian to the end of the last ice age.

Today's Research—Tomorrow's Exhibits

The scientific work that Royal Tyrrell Museum palaeontologists undertake today, both in the field and in the lab, becomes the exhibits that visitors experience tomorrow. With each new discovery, our understanding of the past changes, and the Museum regularly updates its displays to ensure they contain the latest information.

[50]

[49]

One of the most exciting things
about the field of palaeontology
is that every day there is the possibility
of a new discovery—a new species or a new idea
to challenge the prevailing thinking within
the world's scientific community.

Bringing the Past to Life

An understanding of palaeontology requires a comprehension of time that initially is bewildering. One of the best tools to aid our grasp of this concept is the geologic time scale.* This internationally recognized scale uses significant events in the history of life on Earth, such as mass extinctions, to divide and subdivide geologic time into eons, eras, periods, epochs and ages. Museum exhibits refer to these defined units of geologic time or deep time.

Through re-created environments, dynamic displays, hands-on activities and living exhibits, the Royal Tyrrell Museum takes visitors on a journey through time and reveals what life was like on Earth millions of years ago.

[fig 49] *Detail of* Burgess Shale Research Station *exhibit.*

[fig 50] Coelurosauravus, *a gliding reptile from the Permian.*

[fig 51] *The* Cretaceous Alberta *exhibit welcomes visitors to the Museum.*

* *A current geologic time scale is included inside the back cover of this publication, for reference.*

[51]

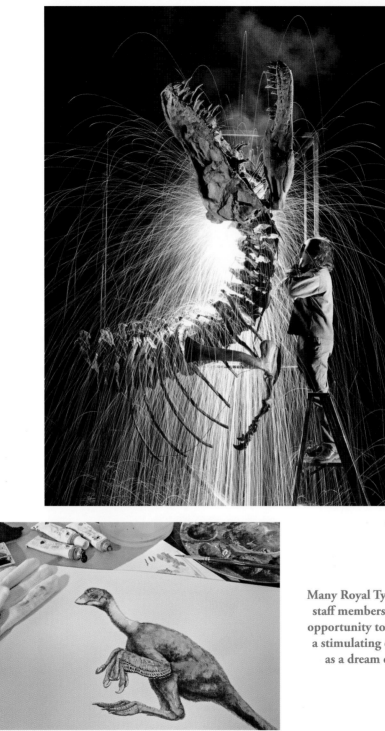

[52]

[53]

Many Royal Tyrrell Museum
staff members describe the
opportunity to work in such
a stimulating environment
as a dream come true.

A Passion for the Past

The Royal Tyrrell Museum is exceptional in many ways. As a destination attraction located some distance from a major city, the Museum is, by necessity, a self-sufficient facility where exhibits are developed, produced, and updated in-house. It is very rare for the Museum to bring in an exhibit from another institution; as a world leader in the field of palaeontology, the Museum focuses much of its content on research that is happening on site.

To achieve this self-sufficiency and to ensure standards of excellence are met, the Museum employs a variety of talented people. Technicians, who assist in prospecting and collecting fossils for study, also provide the expertise and care required to mount specimens for display. A collections team keeps the tens of thousands of specimens organized and safe. Designers, artists, fabricators and writers bring fossils to life with images, illustrations, dioramas and stories. Museum educators connect lifelong learners to the wonders of natural history, while gallery staff guide visitors as they journey through time. And that's just to name a few!

[fig 52] *A technician welds a support for a cast of "Black Beauty," one of the world's most famous* T. rex *skeletons, Drumheller, 1992. The original skeleton and skull are displayed at the Museum—the fossil skull alone weighs 273 kg (600 lbs).*

[fig 53] *Palaeo-artist Julius Csotonyi's image of* Chirostenotes.

[fig 54] *Prepared fossil specimens in storage, labelled and categorized.*

[54]

Cretaceous Alberta

Inspired by work conducted by Royal Tyrrell Museum scientists at Dry Island Buffalo Jump Provincial Park in central Alberta, this gallery features four incredible *Albertosaurus*. *Cretaceous Alberta* immerses visitors in Alberta's semi-tropical landscape of 69 million years ago. *Albertosaurus* was the top predator of its time, and was a close relative of *Tyrannosaurus rex*, which lived a few million years later. The first *Albertosaurus* was discovered by J.B. Tyrrell in 1884.

[56]

[57]

[**fig 56, 57, 58**] *Details of* Cretaceous Alberta *gallery, showing animals that existed in Alberta 70-65 million years ago: an* Albertosaurus, *a turtle,* Aspideretoides, *and a small mammal, the marsupial* Didelphodon.

Cretaceous Garden

The garden is Canada's largest living collection of relatives of prehistoric plants, and includes more than 300 species. This rare collection allows researchers to study environmental change through time by comparing prehistoric plant fossils with plants that live today.

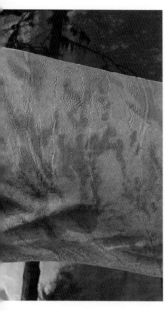

[58]

[60]

This lush, green oasis is a living exhibit showcasing the kinds of plants that dinosaurs dined on 70-65 million years ago.

[fig 59] *Fiddlehead*

[fig 60] *Sago bark*

[fig 61] *Natural light streams in to the* Cretaceous Garden.

[61]

Lords of the Land

Lords of the Land is an intriguing
mix of science and art. This gallery
highlights some of the most rare
and scientifically significant pieces
from the Museum's collection. From
agile raptors perched atop pedestals
to dramatic death poses elegantly
encased by gilded frames, these
creatures are nature's works of art.

These pieces are irreplaceable;
they are priceless *Mona Lisas*
of the natural world.

[**fig 62**] *One of the
Museum's three mounted
T. rex skeletons frames
the title of the exhibit.*

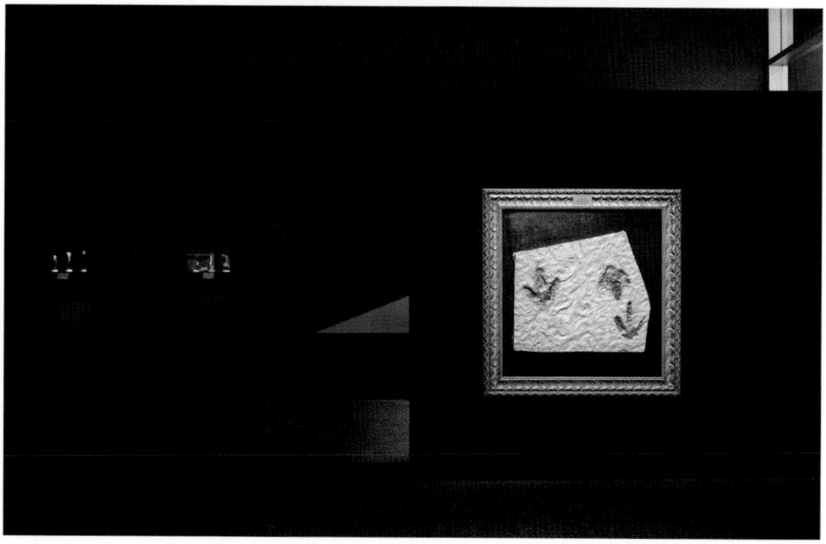

[**fig 63**] *An ornate
gilded frame showcases
Atrociraptor marshalli;
a beautiful holotype found
near the Museum.*

[**fig 64**] *Ornithomimid
tracks preserved in sandstone
are as captivating as any
abstract painting.*

[64]

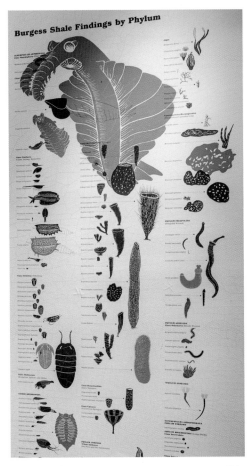

Burgess Shale Findings by Phylum

[66]

Burgess Shale

This exhibit features creatures from the Burgess Shale UNESCO World Heritage site in British Columbia, Canada—one of the most important fossil resources ever found. Immersed in a 505-million-year-old underwater world, visitors come face-to-face with these bizarre creatures enlarged to 12 times their actual size.

[65]

[fig 65] *A detail of the Burgess Shale exhibit presents an illustrated classification chart.*

[fig 66] *Oversize Cambrian creatures can be seen through glass—both at eye level and, more eerily, underfoot.*

[fig 67] *A 1990 Canadian postage stamp depicts one species of trilobite. Trilobite fossils are abundant in the Burgess Shale.*

[67]

Devonian Reef

Around 375 million years ago, Alberta was completely underwater. This portrayal of an undersea reef from the Devonian features life-like creatures that were its inhabitants. Incredible to imagine, the remains of these ancient plankton, modified by time, heat, and pressure, are today the source of Alberta's billion-dollar fossil fuel industry.

[fig 68] *With a proliferation in the number of fish species, the Devonian Period is often referred to as the Age of Fishes.*

[68]

[69]

The majority of fossils found
in Alberta are from the Cretaceous Period.
To tell a more complete story, exhibits
include examples from other geologic
times, from sites all over the world.

[70]

[fig 70] *A partial* Pachyrhinosaurus *skeleton is mounted in front of a complete scientific illustration in the ceratopsian gallery.*

[fig 71] Gorgosaurus *lived during the Cretaceous Period.*

[71]

Dinosaur Hall

This exhibit houses one of the world's largest displays of dinosaur remains. With everything from the easily recognized herbivore, *Stegosaurus*, to the breathtaking *Tyrannosaurus rex*, visitors can marvel at just how amazing these creatures were.

After the Dinosaurs

The Museum continues the story of life on Earth with exhibits depicting the Age of Mammals and the ice age, parts of the Cenozoic Era.

[fig 69] *This skull of* Estemmenosuchus, *a large-bodied plant eater from the Permian, was discovered in Russia.*

Wonder

To be surprised,
to wonder, is to begin
to understand.
JOSE ORTEGA Y GASSET

Connecting
to the World

*Science from the Royal Tyrrell Museum
is changing the way the world thinks
about evolution, extinction, biodiversity,
climate change, and the future.*

Global Connections and Collaborations

The Royal Tyrrell Museum's research, researchers, and collections are in great demand the world over. Museum scientists collaborate with other museums, universities, and research centres.

By studying the wealth of material in their own "backyard," Museum scientists are able to make significant contributions to the world beyond.

[fig 72] *Dinosaur Provincial Park visitor centre.*

[fig 73] UNESCO World Heritage Site *logo*.

More than 30 museums around the world display fossils found in Dinosaur Provincial Park.

[73]

[72]

Royal Tyrrell Museum Field Station at Dinosaur Provincial Park—UNESCO World Heritage Site

Dinosaur Provincial Park is situated 175 kilometres southeast of the Royal Tyrrell Museum in the Alberta badlands. Established in 1955, the Park was designated a UNESCO World Heritage Site in 1979.

In 1987, a visitor centre opened in Dinosaur Provincial Park. This facility assists in the preservation of fossil resources, exhibits significant finds and presents displays regarding the geology and natural history of the Park. Royal Tyrrell Museum researchers have worked in the Park for many years, and the Dinosaur Provincial Park visitor centre functions as a permanent field station.

Cast Across the Globe

In the early twentieth century, great amounts
of fossil material from Alberta left the province
to be studied and to build the collections of museums
around the world. Today, researchers across the globe
study casts (exact replicas) of fossils housed in the
Royal Tyrrell Museum collection. Since more than
one cast can be made from an original fossil, the
entire scientific community benefits, as researchers
in different locations can study identical specimens.

[74]

[**fig 74**] *A visiting Ph.D.
student at the Royal Tyrrell
Museum creates a mold of
the teeth of* Lambeosaurus
lambei *to make a cast for
further study. The resulting
replica will reveal different
microscopic wear patterns;
indicating how and what
this herbivorous dinosaur
might have eaten.*

Great Expeditions

In addition to the Alberta badlands, there are a number of other "fossil hotspots" around the world. Royal Tyrrell Museum scientists have worked in the Canadian High Arctic, China, Mongolia, Mexico, Antarctica, and several countries in Europe and South America.

[fig 75] *"Expedition Mongolia," Khermeen Tsav, Mongolia, 2009.*

[75]

World Tour for a Prized *T. rex*

In the 1990s, millions of years after it took its last stride in the Late Cretaceous, "Black Beauty" became a well-known international traveller visiting Canada, Japan, Singapore and Australia as part of the ExTerra Foundation's Dinosaur World Tour. In 2010, "Black Beauty" emerged from storage to star in the Museum's 25th anniversary exhibit, *Alberta Unearthed*. With this addition, the Royal Tyrrell Museum became the only museum in the world to display three *T. rex* skeletons.

[76]

[**fig 76**] *Souvenir coin from the ExTerra Foundation Dinosaur World Tour.*

[**fig 77**] *The Museum calls this stunning* Tyrannosaurus rex *skeleton "Black Beauty." During fossilization, manganese in the soil caused the bones to turn a rare, dark hue.*

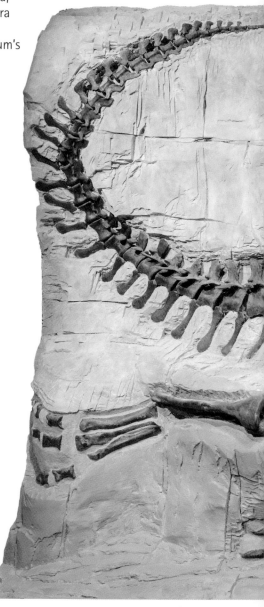

Getting the Word Out

Media from around the world regularly call on the Royal Tyrrell Museum, Canada's dinosaur authority. Scientists provide expertise that supports the production of educational and entertaining television programs and films for audiences young and old.

As one of Canada's premier tourist attractions, the Museum is also often featured in tourism-related media as one of the world's must-see destinations.

While the basic method of uncovering fossils has changed little in the past century, the ability to share information and collaborate with others has changed dramatically.

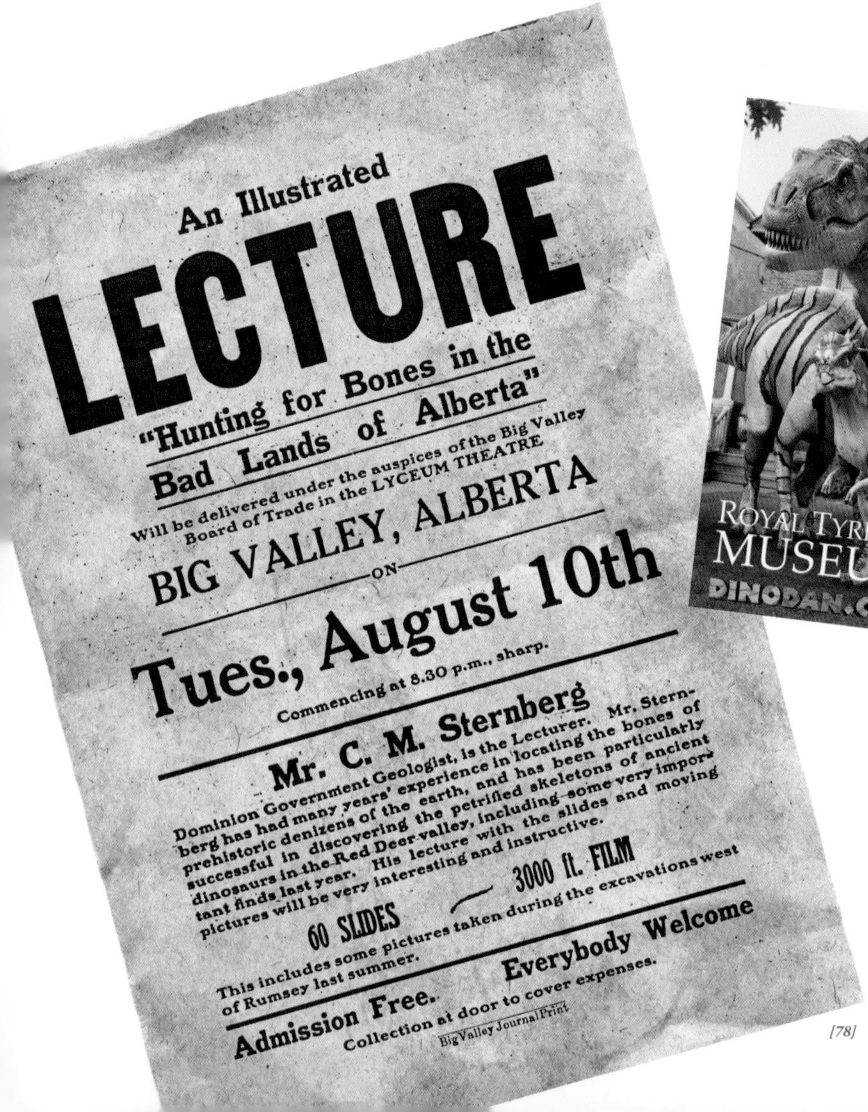

[79]

An Illustrated LECTURE

"Hunting for Bones in the Bad Lands of Alberta"

Will be delivered under the auspices of the Big Valley Board of Trade in the LYCEUM THEATRE

BIG VALLEY, ALBERTA

—ON—

Tues., August 10th

Commencing at 8.30 p.m., sharp.

Mr. C. M. Sternberg

Mr. Sternberg has had many years' experience in locating the bones of prehistoric denizens of the earth, and has been particularly successful in discovering the petrified skeletons of ancient dinosaurs in the Red Deer valley, including some very important finds last year. His lecture with the slides and moving pictures will be very interesting and instructive.

60 SLIDES — 3000 ft. FILM

This includes some pictures taken during the excavations west of Rumsey last summer.

Admission Free. Everybody Welcome.

Collection at door to cover expenses.

Big Valley Journal Print

[78]

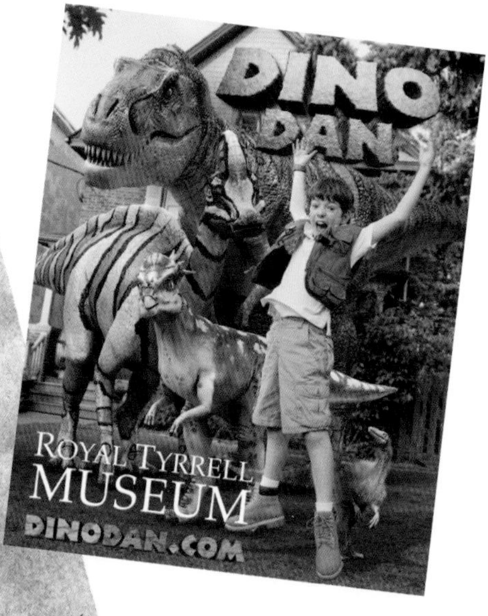

[fig 78] *Poster for presentation given by Charles M. Sternberg in the village of Big Valley, Alberta in 1925.*

[fig 79] *The Royal Tyrrell Museum collaborated with Sinking Ship Entertainment on the children's show Dino Dan. This incredibly popular series reaches 90 million viewers.*

[fig 80] *The haunting and beautiful Alberta badlands.*

An Exceptional Place

More than 100 years after the first fossil hunters made their way to Alberta, people continue to be drawn to the badlands—arriving full of curiosity, and leaving with a renewed sense of wonder about time and the natural world.

Since opening its doors to the public in 1985, the Royal Tyrrell Museum has dedicated itself to celebrating the history and amazing diversity of life on Earth—from the tiniest grain of pollen to the mightiest dinosaur. Internationally recognized for its innovative research, vast collections, and dynamic galleries, the Museum captures the hearts and minds of all who walk through its doors.

ENDNOTES

1. Martin J. S. Rudwick, *Worlds before Adam: The Reconstruction of Geohistory in the Age of Reform* (Chicago, IL: The University of Chicago Press, 2008) 48.

2. Michael Newbrey Ph.D., Royal Tyrrell Museum scientist, February 2010.

3. *Dinosaur and Paleontology Dictionary*, "Sir Richard Owen," 16 February 2010. <http://www.enchantedlearning.com/subjects/dinosaurs/glossary/Owen.shtml>.

4. Jill Roberts, *Finders: A Century of Fossil Hunting in Alberta* (Drumheller, AB: Royal Tyrrell Museum of Palaeontology, 2005) 6.

5. Jill Roberts, *Finders: A Century of Fossil Hunting in Alberta* (Drumheller, AB: Royal Tyrrell Museum of Palaeontology, 2005) 6.

6. Geological Survey of Canada, "Past lives: Chronicles of Canadian Paleontology—Peigans, Buffalo and Fossils," 22 March 2010 <http://gsc.nrcan.gc.ca/paleochron/30_e.php>.

7. Phil Jenkins, *Beneath My Feet: The Memoirs of George Mercer Dawson* (Toronto, ON: McClelland & Stewart, 2007) 204.

8. Dave Birrell, "Dawson, George M.," *Peak Finder*, 19 March 2010. <http://peakfinder.com/people.asp?[PersonsName]=dawson%2C+george>.

9. Jill Roberts, *Finders: A Century of Fossil Hunting in Alberta* (Drumheller, AB: Royal Tyrrell Museum of Palaeontology, 2005) 8.

10. Dave Birrell, "Naming the Peaks of the Canadian Rockies: George Dawson," *Peak Finder*, 19 March 2010 <http://www.rmbooks.com/Peakfinder/namingpeaks.htm>.

11. Geological Survey of Canada, "Sir William Logan 1798–1875: Logan and Canada's Museums," 31 May 2010 <http://gsc.nrcan.gc.ca/hist/logan/museum_e.php>.

12. Martin K. McNicholl, "Tyrrell, Joseph Burr," *The Canadian Encyclopedia* 10 March 2010 <http://www.thecanadianencyclopedia.com/index.cfm?PgNm=TCE&Params=A1ARTA0008186>.

13. Heather Robertson, *Measuring Mother Earth: How Joe the Kid Became Tyrrell of the North* (Toronto, ON: McClelland & Stewart, 2007) 59.

14. 19 March 2010 <http://academic.emporia.edu/aberjame/histgeol/stern/stern1.jpg>.

15. Charles Hazelius Sternberg, *Hunting dinosaurs in the bad lands of the Red Deer River, Alberta, Canada: A sequel to The Life of a Fossil Hunter* (Lawrence, KS, 1917) 35.

16. Charles Hazelius Sternberg, *Hunting dinosaurs in the bad lands of the Red Deer River, Alberta, Canada: A sequel to The Life of a Fossil Hunter* (Lawrence, KS, 1917) 207.

17. David Spalding, *Into the Dinosaurs' Graveyard: Canadian Digs and Discoveries* (Toronto, ON: Doubleday Canada, 1999) 143.

18. Charles Hazelius Sternberg, *Hunting dinosaurs in the bad lands of the Red Deer River, Alberta, Canada: A sequel to The Life of a Fossil Hunter* (Lawrence, KS, 1917) 205.

IMAGE ACKNOWLEDGEMENTS

Royal Tyrrell Museum Library Collection (RTMLC)

Thedor Erkamps and Owen Melenka (TE/OM)

Others as noted.

opposite Foreword: Model *Albertosaurus* outside the Royal Tyrrell Museum. RTMLC

page 5: Red Deer River, Alberta. RTMLC

page 6: Illustrations by Julius Csotonyi. RTMLC

page 7: Illustrated map by Teresa McLaren

page 8: Sir Richard Owen (1804-1892). © The Natural History Museum, London, image #1350

page 9: left: Group of Blackfoot Confederacy men [ca. middle 1880s]. Glenbow Archives NA-2968-4. right: Illustration by Julius Csotonyi

page 10: top: Uphill hauling. Courtesy of Natural Resources Canada, photo #GSC 40017. bottom: G. Sternberg with *Chasmosaurus* skull. RTMLC

page 11: top: Philatelic image: Registered letter stamp, 5¢, 15 November 1875. © Canada Post Corporation (1875), reproduced with permission. bottom: Steveville. Glenbow Archives, NA-48-1

page 12: top: Canadian International Boundary Commission Staff, 1872. Glenbow Archives, NA-249-1. bottom: Geological Survey of Canada photograph archive stamp. RTMLC

page 14: top: J.B. Tyrrell portrait, 1880s. Thomas Fisher Rare Book Library, University of Toronto, J.B. Tyrrell papers. bottom: J.B. Tyrrell Historical Medal, courtesy of Dr. David Bercuson. TE/OM

page 15: top: *Albertosaurus* skull discovered by J.B. Tyrrell in 1884. RTMLC. bottom: detail, Geological map of part of northern Alberta and portions of the Districts of Assiniboia and Saskatchewan, North West Territory. Ottawa: Geological and Natural History Survey of Canada, 1887, by J.B. Tyrrell. Glenbow Library and Archives. photographed by TE/OM

page 16: Packing specimens. RTMLC

page 17: top left: Sternberg party on Red Deer River, photograph by Barnum Brown. American Museum of Natural History, #18547. middle left: Levi Sternberg jacketing fossil. RTMLC. bottom: Sternberg and Abbott excavating

Royal Tyrrell Museum. TE/OM

bones of fossil Duck Billed Dinosaur *Hadrosaur*, Sand Creek Basin–Belly River Formation, Alberta, 6/1/1922. The Field Museum, negative #CSGEO45072

page 18: Unidentified children and tourist information sign near Drumheller, Alberta, 1958. Provincial Archives of Alberta #A734987

page 21: Main entrance of the Royal Tyrrell Museum. RTMLC

page 22: *Cretaceous Alberta* exhibit detail. TE/OM

page 23: top: Badlands landscape. middle: "Popcorn rock." bottom: illustration of prehistoric fern. RTMLC

page 24: Midland Coal Mine. Glenbow Archives NA-2389-67

page 25: top: Kathryn and Ross Bailey, Drumheller, Alberta, 1973. Photograph by Edwin R. Bailey. bottom left: Drumheller Coal advertisement, ca. 1970. bottom right: Unidentified man in Drumheller. Provincial Archives of Alberta, #A8585

page 26: top, middle: Moving dinosaur skeletons, 1985. bottom: Elevation drawing, 1982. RTMLC.

page 27: The Royal Tyrrell Museum. RTMLC

page 31: *Archaeopteryx* fossil. TE/OM

page 32: Specimens in lab. TE/OM

page 33: left: *Albertosaurus* leg bones, mounted, ca. 1915. Glenbow Archives NA-3250-14. right: Pollen *Accuratipollis macrosolenoides*. RTMLC

page 34: top: Quarry marker. bottom: Specimen label. RTMLC

page 35: Helicopter lifting specimen. RTMLC

page 36: Specimens in storage. TE/OM

page 37: top: Preparation station. bottom: Specimens organized in boxes. TE/OM

page 38: Field notebook. TE/OM

page 39: top: Door to Type Storage. TE/OM. bottom: *Eotriceratops* skull. RTMLC

page 40: G. Sternberg packing fossils, 1921. Courtesy of Natural Resources Canada, photo #GSC 40012

page 41: top: *Platypterygius americanus*. bottom: Quarry marker. RTMLC

page 43: Juvenile *Albertosaurus*, *Cretaceous Alberta* exhibit. TE/OM

page 44: left: detail of *Burgess Shale Research Station* exhibit. top right: *Coelurosauravus*. TE/OM

page 45: *Cretaceous Alberta* exhibit. TE/OM

page 46: top: "A *Tyrannosaurus rex* skeleton gets a lift from a welded support frame. Photograph by Louie Psihoyos, Science Faction. bottom: Illustration of *Chirostenotes* by Julius Csotonyi. TE/OM

page 47: Specimens in storage. TE/OM

page 48: details of *Cretaceous Alberta* exhibit. TE/OM

page 49: details of *Cretaceous Garden* exhibit. RTMLC

page 50, 51: details of *Lords of the Land* exhibit. TE/OM

page 52: top left: detail of *Burgess Shale* exhibit. TE/OM. top right: detail of *Burgess Shale* exhibit. RTMLC bottom: Philatelic image: *Paradoxides davidis*, Trilobite, Cambrian Period, 39¢, 12 July 1990. © Canada Post Corporation (1990), reproduced with permission.

page 53: detail of *Devonian Reef* exhibit. TE/OM

page 54: *Estemmenosuchus* skull. TE/OM

page 55: details of *Dinosaur Hall* exhibits. TE/OM

page 59: Shipping crate containing baby hadrosaur skeleton, in storage. TE/OM

page 60: Dinosaur Provincial Park visitor centre. RTMLC

page 62: Jordan Mallon making a mold of specimen in *Dinosaur Hall* exhibit, 2010. TE/OM

page 63: Gobi Desert. RTMLC

page 64, 65: ExTerra Souvenir Coin, "Black Beauty" fossil skeleton. TE/OM

page 66: Poster for C.M. Sternberg lecture, 1925. (image modified). Glenbow Archives, Sternberg Fonds. *Dino Dan* poster, Sinking Ship Entertainment

page 67: Badlands landscape. RTMLC

inside back cover: detail, Geological map of part of northern Alberta and portions of the Districts of Assiniboia and Saskatchewan, North West Territory. Ottawa: Geological and Natural History Survey of Canada, 1887, by J.B. Tyrrell, Glenbow Library and Archives. Photographed by TE/OM. back cover flap, inside: Illustrated geologic time scale by Teresa McLaren

INDEX

Numbers in italic refer to images.

cont'd. next page

INDEX cont'd.

*This 1887 geologic map by J.B. Tyrrell
includes the site of the Museum that
would bear his name over a century
later. Fossil sites are indicated by
this symbol.*